WHERE'S THE MAGICAL UNICORN POOP?

SCHOLASTIC

LET THE SEARCH BEGIN!

Stardust City is home to hundreds of cool creatures. There are unicorns, mermaids, llamas and narwhals, plus mermicorns and llamacorns, too! It's a world of happiness, harmony, friendship and glitter – but today the creatures are in a panic. An explosion at Stardust Sewage Works has opened a magical portal and washed the contents of the city's toilets all the way into our world. Unicorn poop has plopped down all over the planet!

The embarrassed creatures have set out on an adventure to clean up the mess. Can you help them find the shimmering swirls?

There are **NINE** magical, rainbow-coloured unicorn poops to spot in each scene, along with **ONE** super-special golden poop. Your journey will take you across the globe, from the bustling streets of Tokyo to the canals of Venice.

RAINBOW UNICORN POOP

SPECIAL GOLDEN POOP

Ready to get flushed away on a search-and-find adventure?

5

POOP SEARCH PARTY

Meet the creatures on the hunt for the missing poops! They'll journey around the world, using magical portals in public toilets to travel from place to place. They hope to squeeze in some sightseeing, too. Keep an eye out for the entire team in every scene.

CORAL CONCH

A mermaid on a mission! Coral's excellent organizational skills are sure to help the team in their search for the unicorn poop.

Loves: synchronized swimming
Hates: single-use plastics

BORIS BRIGHTBILL

Witty Boris is brilliant at making his friends laugh and can turn even the grumpiest frown upside down. He's bound to keep the other creatures feeling cheerful on their journey.

Loves: one-liners
Hates: TV talent shows

TINA TIDETROT

Tina the mermicorn is an incredible artist – her hoof-print paintings are always in demand. She's hoping to find some inspiration for future projects on this mission.

Loves: mane makeovers
Hates: sushi

ROSIE ROCOCO

Rosie is the fanciest flamingo in the flock. She loves cream teas, garden parties and afternoons perusing posh boutiques. She's hoping not to get her wings dirty!

Loves: flower arranging
Hates: fast fashion

SID SLOWCLAW

Sid is an adrenaline junkie! Bungee jumping, skydiving, swimming with sharks – you name it, he's tried it! He's looking forward to soaring through the skies on an epic poop-finding adventure.

Loves: roller coasters
Hates: noisy eaters

DANA VON DAZZLE

Dana is a unicorn with a passion for all things edible! She can often be found rustling up her own original recipes or out and about sampling Stardust City's best street food.

Loves: unusual ingredients
Hates: beans on toast

WILMA WOOLLY

Fitness fanatic Wilma is a llama who is totally obsessed with sports. She's preparing for an ultra-marathon and hopes to get in some training during the trip.

Loves: cosy knitwear
Hates: long queues

ALI AIRWING

An alicorn with attitude! Ali loves the spotlight – he's the first on the dance floor and the last to be dragged off it.

Loves: cheesy pop music
Hates: guitar solos

GARY MCGALLOP

Gary is the friendliest llamacorn in Stardust City, always ready to lend a helping hoof or offer some words of wisdom to neighbours in need.

Loves: writing letters
Hates: custard

NIGEL NOSEHORN

Nigel the narwhal is fascinated by history. The most well-read resident of Stardust City, he can't wait to visit some of the famous locations from his books.

Loves: cryptic crosswords
Hates: musicals

TRAFALGAR SQUARE ● LONDON ● ENGLAND

CITY SIGHTS

The unicorn poop search party has arrived in Trafalgar Square, one of London's busiest places. Nelson's Column towers above the tourists as they go about their day, while buskers entertain the crowds below.

Ali the alicorn is picking up some tricks from the street performers, while fancy flamingo, Rosie, is wondering whether anyone will notice if she pops to the shops for a couple of hours. But mermaid-in-charge, Coral, is keen to keep the team focused – they've got poop to clean up!

ARTY PARTY

When the creatures arrive in Paris, there's a long line outside the Louvre, the world's largest art museum. The people are here to see paintings, not poop! The creatures better find it all – fast.

Tina the mermicorn is looking forward to exploring the gallery and admiring some masterpieces, while Dana the unicorn plans to sample a Parisian pastry or two. Meanwhile, the others are doing their best to discover the doo-doos. Can you help them out by spotting all ten unicorn poops on the page?

THE LOUVRE • PARIS • FRANCE

THE GRAND CANAL • VENICE • ITALY

CANAL CAPER

The unicorn poop search party has landed in Venice! The Italian city is criss-crossed by four hundred bridges, connecting over one hundred islands.

Nigel the narwhal is doing his best not to knock into a gondola, one of Venice's special boats, as he splashes through the canals. Ali is off to buy a Venetian mask for his next fancy-dress party, the more colourful and sparkly the better. Speaking of sparkly, ten magical unicorn poops are glittering in the sunlight – see if you can spot them!

PARK GÜELL ● BARCELONA ● SPAIN

POOP IN THE PARK

High on a hill above sunny Barcelona, a pretty Spanish park has been invaded by unicorn poop! The search party must hunt high and low among the swaying palm trees, colourful columns and eye-catching architecture. Can you give them a hand?

There are plenty of treetops for Boris the toucan to explore, and exercise addict Wilma the llama has already sprinted a couple of laps around the gardens!

AMERICAN ADVENTURE

The Washington Monument is a towering 169-metre pillar, built in memory of the first president of the United States. Down below, the creatures are exploring the grounds, brushing up on their history and keeping a lookout for unicorn poop!

Nigel is in his element – there's so much to see and learn – but Coral's worried the group will get lost in the crowd. Can you help her round everyone up?

WASHINGTON MONUMENT ● WASHINGTON D.C. ● UNITED STATES

FORBIDDEN CITY • BEIJING • CHINA

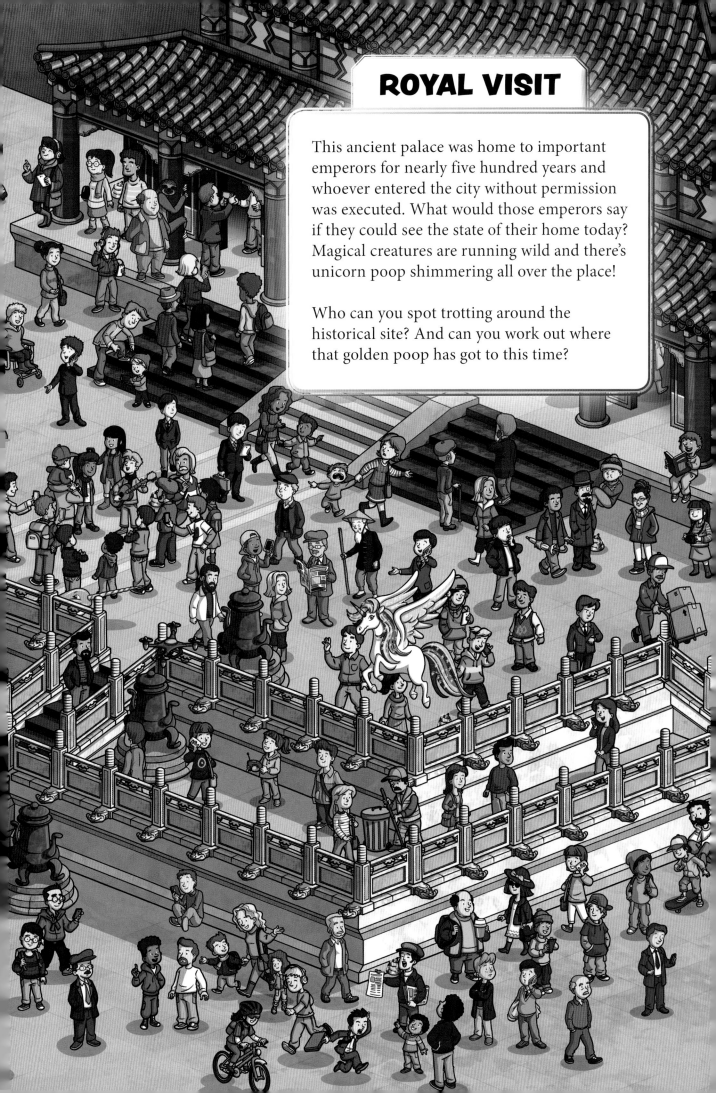

ROYAL VISIT

This ancient palace was home to important emperors for nearly five hundred years and whoever entered the city without permission was executed. What would those emperors say if they could see the state of their home today? Magical creatures are running wild and there's unicorn poop shimmering all over the place!

Who can you spot trotting around the historical site? And can you work out where that golden poop has got to this time?

SYDNEY HARBOUR • SYDNEY • AUSTRALIA

DOWN UNDER

More unicorn poop has popped up – or rather, plopped down – in Sydney Harbour! The creatures are excited to visit Australia, home to heaps of animals *almost* as cool as them, including koalas, kangaroos and crocodiles.

Gary the llamacorn is getting to know the locals, while Ali the alicorn is off to buy a ticket for the next performance at Sydney Opera House. Perhaps they'll even let him sing on stage!

FLOATING MARKET ● MEKONG DELTA ● VIETNAM

MARKET MAYHEM

This floating market just got a little more magical. There are so many interesting things to discover, with boats selling everything from delicious fruits to fragrant spices, beautiful plants to handmade pots. But that golden poop is not for sale!

Rosie the flamingo has spotted some pretty material she thinks would make the perfect tablecloth. Meanwhile, Tina the mermicorn is itching to get her hooves on her paints and capture the scene.

FESTIVAL OF COLOUR

During the special Holi festival, bright paints and powders are thrown all over the place as people come together to celebrate! The magical unicorn poops might be harder to spot in all the colourful commotion.

Boris the toucan is enjoying the excitement, but Rosie's feathers are getting ruffled – she doesn't want to end up as a bright blue flamingo. Who else can you spot in the scene?

HOLI FESTIVAL ● MUMBAI ● INDIA

TIVOLI GARDENS ● COPENHAGEN ● DENMARK

RIDING ROLLER COASTERS

Copenhagen's world-famous theme park is packed with thrill-seekers. There's a gigantic roller coaster, a Ferris wheel and bumper cars, plus music and dance performances. It's no wonder the creatures keep getting distracted with so much to see and do!

Sid the sloth has ridden the roller coaster so many times he is beginning to feel a little queasy! Boris the toucan is hoping to catch some comedy on one of the many stages and Dana the unicorn is visiting the food stalls to try some Danish delicacies.

SHIBUYA CROSSING ● TOKYO ● JAPAN

TOKYO TRAFFIC

Tokyo is one of the busiest capital cities in the world, bustling with over thirteen million residents! The streets are packed with people rushing here and there. Caught up in the commotion, the creatures are having a hard time picking up unicorn poop.

Gary the llamacorn has helped eight old ladies cross the road and now he's lost the rest of the search party! Can you see where Rosie, Ali, Boris and the others have got to?

CARNIVAL CHAOS

Welcome to Brazil's liveliest, loudest and most colourful celebration! As the drums begin to play, enormous floats travel through the stadium, accompanied by performers in spectacular sparkling costumes. Let's hope none of the dancers step in any doo-doos…

Alongside the parade, Ali the alicorn is practising his samba steps, while Rosie the flamingo is admiring the headdresses. She hopes nobody pinches one of her tail feathers for their hat though!

RIO CARNIVAL ● RIO DE JANEIRO ● BRAZIL

NIAGARA FALLS ● ONTARIO ● CANADA

WATERFALL RUSH

Over 28 million litres of water crash over Niagara Falls each second! This natural wonder sits on the border between the United States and Canada and attracts millions of visitors from all over the world. This time, it has visitors from out of this world, too.

Sid the sloth has heard that a few daredevils have completed tightrope walks across the falls. He's thinking of trying it himself… Tina the mermicorn is happy to just splash back and enjoy the view.

SCOTTISH SEARCH

The creatures have reached the capital of Scotland, where an exciting festival is underway. Around every street corner a poetry reading or theatre performance is taking place. But with magical unicorn poop mucking up the cobbled streets, the creatures might not have time to enjoy all the culture!

Boris the toucan has heard his favourite comedian is in town and plans to pop off to watch him perform. But there's not long to go before the creatures need to head home – can you help them clean up Edinburgh's streets?

fringe

EDINBURGH FESTIVAL FRINGE ● EDINBURGH ● SCOTLAND

MAKING WAVES

As tourists explore the dramatic landscape in Northern Ireland, the creatures are combing the stones for unicorn poop! These columns were created millions of years ago, when fiery volcanic activity forced the rocks into strange shapes. As if the scene wasn't weird enough, it's now overrun with llamas, sloths, mermaids and more.

Nigel the narwhal is looking to pick up an audio guide and discover the site's history. But Rosie the flamingo isn't enjoying the cold climate – help the search party find the poop before she gets too chilly.

GIANT'S CAUSEWAY ● COUNTY ANTRIM ● NORTHERN IRELAND

BERGEN ● NORWAY

MOUNTAIN MISSION

Nestled in the Norwegian mountains, the steep streets of Bergen are lined with colourful houses and shops. A cold sea breeze sweeps through the city as the creatures begin their search.

Wilma the llama wants to head off on a hike to explore, but Coral the mermaid is feeling homesick – she's keen to get back to Stardust City as soon as possible. Where have those magical unicorn poops got to this time?

WINTER MARKET • NUREMBERG • GERMANY

FESTIVE FUN

The mission is almost over – the search party have just one more place to clean up. A festive market fills the square of this German city, with stalls selling everything from slippers to sausages!

As Rosie the flamingo shops for some last-minute souvenirs, Dana the unicorn is enjoying the delicious gingerbread and dreaming up her own version of the recipe. It's nearly time to go home though, just ten more poops to find!

ANSWERS

CITY SIGHTS

ARTY PARTY

CANAL CAPERS

POOP IN THE PARK

42

AMERICAN ADVENTURE

ROYAL VISIT

DOWN UNDER

MARKET MAYHEM

FESTIVAL OF COLOUR

RIDING ROLLER COASTERS

DID YOU FIND THE SEARCH PARTY?

There are 10 characters to find in each scene.
Place a tick next to each character after you've found them in all the scenes.

TOKYO TRAFFIC

CARNIVAL CHAOS

WATERFALL RUSH

SCOTTISH SEARCH

MAKING WAVES

MOUNTAIN MISSION

FESTIVE FUN

Published in the UK by Scholastic Children's Books, 2020
Euston House, 24 Eversholt Street, London, NW1 1DB
A division of Scholastic Ltd

London ~ New York ~ Toronto ~ Sydney ~ Auckland
Mexico City ~ New Delhi ~ Hong Kong

Written by Emily Hibbs © Scholastic Children's Books, 2020
Illustrations by Pablo Gallego with contributions from Jorge Santillan,
Anthony Rule and Martyn Cain (Beehive Illustration) © Scholastic Children's Books, 2020

Trade hardback edition ISBN 978 1407 19832 3
Scholastic Clubs and Fairs paperback edition ISBN 978 0702 30155 1

A CIP catalogue record for this book is available from the British Library.

Printed in Malaysia

2 4 6 8 10 9 7 5 3 1

Papers used by Scholastic Children's Books are
made from wood grown in sustainable forests.

www.scholastic.co.uk